D1396720

THE
LAMP

PATRICIA BRADSHAW

Cover design and book production by Christine Delano.
Cover photograph by Holly Leighanne.
Printed in the United States of America
First Printing, 2013
ISBN 978-0-615-75976-0

To Kathy Keehn

PART I

Chapter One

Dear Fabbie:

Surprise, surprise! I am with you in California, abandoned on the West Coast. Widowed. At large!

Oh, why did you not fall in love with me instead of with that twit you 1st married? I have been worried that you have done it again. I know from the Christmas cards that you married a plain Jane (pardon; I go too far). This letter introduces my intention to find out. Here I come, maybe!

I know I deduce a little bit about her. First, she has lasted already longer than the twit, and you have had children, at least on the cards at Christmas. Further under the heading of "or she wouldn't have lasted", she loves wine, reading, and music listening. Do you still belong to a version of Les Amis de Vin, which Jim said made you look like an English toff?

And she must love Switzerland, since you go every year. Footnote: Notice disquisition on Switzerland and myself at letter's end; An Iowa Swiss Tale.

Nothing bad so far, but then I couldn't believe you picked the first one, either. Do you remember A Perfect Day for Banana Fish, in which Seymour Glass killed himself on the day he was to marry a…. a twit? I really worried about your health! She was so far unlike my image of you. Well, do you want to know my image of you? I should've told you years ago, but we were way too cool to discuss personal things. So: I have never met anyone else who lived up to the way people **should** live under Capitalism/Democracy. You took everything it offered in our free public high school, not skipping the hard stuff: Chemistry (you told me to blow into the cone of carbon we were given, damn you); Geometry (remember Billy Gage writing those awful formulae on the tiny flats of his pencils, to use in exams).

Remember we liked arts and humanities. That revelatory English class where we actually memorized Invictus and the crowd of daffodils! And hated Silas Marner!

After high school, to my surprise, you went to Ames. General Engineering. Somebody was telling you that you would have to earn a good living if you wanted to maintain your standard of wine-living. By the way did you read Jane Smiley's book about Ames? I liked it.

See Fabio and Claudia diverge, alas, though we met in summer for our platonic walks on the Palisades of a Saturday or Sunday afternoon, talking about what each was reading. Plato, of course. I never understood why Plato wasn't heaved out for elitism, at the very least. Kant, believe it! I remember one of us smarted off in class that "Kant never did anything". **You** did!

G.B. Shaw. The days Jim was along, we discussed endlessly the Letters of Holmes and Pollock, which I never read. We did not discuss Engineering.

Then the War. I was in New York at Columbia grad school and you came to see me in my digs there. Now, you're afraid I'm going to remind you of that tipsy night in my small room, but I won't. Or will I? Anyway, then you came again through New York and New Jersey to visit my husband and 2 kids and me. There was one crawling baby you took to, who grew up to be mysteriously like you. Then I brought all four children and a husband to our hometown, where you gave a party for us. Where all the wives studiously knitted, looking down at their laps and giving me the cold-shoulder. Jim's wife, too, but especially the twit, for whom you later apologized. Those walks on the Palisades were platonic, girls! But they cast an odd shadow.

Or, did "someone" tell about the tipsy night (here goes) in New

York when that standing and also tipsy lamp crashed down on us in the middle of our...test! Experiment? We never considered unmarried and non-child sex, as everyone else did. We were too..."intellectual". But there **was** that night. Ouch. The failure of the experiment was not because of the lamp, but because of wild laughter, when we realized how apt the lamp falling actually was.

The only other time we laughed that whooping, gasping prolonged howling was the time Jim grabbed your hated hat and jumped up and down on it, while our Business School teacher walked in to retrieve his coat and hat. Which hat was **his** hat, identical but not **your** hat.

The look on his face! The look on yours when you pulled that lamp off me! We laughed long and hard; we really got joy of the lamp.

Of course you have e-mail. So e-mail me back and tell all.

Love, Claudia

P.S. A Swiss-Iowa Tale

Do you remember I had a Swiss-born uncle with whose family I spent many summers on his farm? His parents came a bit after he did to the States, specifically to Iowa, where they bought a farm, which was called by my uncle's family and me and the community, The Other Place. My uncle was called (unbelievably for so many years ago) "Dude". At the point when his parents came, Dude quit college and began to farm, too.

His wife, my mother's sister, met him in college and left college with him. He was a hunk! They had a daughter roughly my age, a great opportunity for my mother to farm me out so she could take summertime graduate courses at Madison, Chicago, and other universities who excelled in her field.

The advent of Dude's parents made a new life for everyone involved. They came lock, stock, and barrel—with everything they owned, including A Secret Trunk.

The trunk was placed (hidden!) in an attic, not unpacked, but not forgotten by my cousin and me. We teased, cajoled, and never let it go year after year until finally my aunt (Lucinda, called Lou Lou) said, "You are embarrassing Grandma and Grandpa, and you are driving Dude and me crazy. This has got to stop. You are 15, and ought to be able to keep a secret. I will tell you now, if you will promise never to tell them that you know".

Off course, after the grandparents died the little farm town learned the secret and clamored for the contents of the trunk. Only very special people got one of what was in it.

They had spent years in Switzerland farming Swiss cows, who roamed Swiss mountains. Thoughtfully they brought Swiss cowbells with them for the Iowa cows to wear, so that they would not be lost in Iowa Mountains.

When I finally made it to Switzerland, sitting upon an Alp I heard cowbells ringing all around. I finally sensed the embarrassment of Uncle Dude's parents.

Chapter Two

Dear Claudius,

You must know that I have not changed enough to bear with the infantilizing of my name, hence, the masculinizing of yours. After a lifetime of being named for a great grandfather with an obscure Italian name, (Fabio), while living in **Iowa**, of all non-Italian places, and trying to **be** Iowan. Well, call me Ishmael, but **don't** Fabbie me!

Re the personal remarks: my wife, Jane, is perfect for me, no twit she. The remarks about my character are out of bounds and out of line. Stop that!

I am surprised and delighted to hear from my old pal of the Palisades, and remember well our walks on a Saturday or Sunday afternoon, with Jim or without, and good laughs. Oh my yes! But now is now.

Now. I don't look like the guy you knew so many years ago. No no no, you should not visit. It would spoil good memories. I have had, not too long ago, a heart operation, and I look different. Not bad, but damn different. Oh no, I am not very bald. I am sunken, scrawny, ashen. Don't come. Hear this. Don't come!

And no, I don't have e-mail. I've considered it, but it seems to me, well, to encourage unnecessary speech. It makes for chatting. I know you chat against all odds (I hasten to say it is a part of your charm.) Oh dear, please please don't take offense. Do chat on! Be happy with my—what, restraint? No, I am not proud of it, it is just ingrown.

Tell me you are not taking offense.

Love, Fabio

Chapter Three

Dear Fabio:

Chat, chat, chat, I'm offended, of course. Mad! Chat, chat, chat.

Chat

Chat

Chat

Chat

Chat

Chat

Chat

Chat

Chat

Chat

Chat

Chat

Chat

Chat

Chat

Chat

Chat

Love, Claudia

Chapter Four

Dear Claudia,

Now Claudia, for God's sake, I take it back, I take back everything. I will do everything you want. Everything. How about in exchange for saying "your adorable chatting", my next letter will arrive online, so to speak, that is, Claudia, if you will send me your adorable (is this really me?) email address.

Now!

Dear Claudia. Thank you for that chat. Oops. My email address is as you see on the letter. I have been doing nil but practicing the computer. It is not easy; what the hell, there is no manual; are you supposed to have a techie live-in? I practice (swearing,) losing text, practice, copying, (how about L,l, and 1?) I feel stupid, **being** stupid. All right, I should have learned computereze when I was—When I was not young in some future generation?

Do I thank you? Yes!!!

Seeking insouciance, let us proceed as if I am an adept, please please!

Now, what are you reading, listening to, thinking? I know about drinking. "Vodka, I am here". I mean I am still a wino and assume vodka is still there by your side

What am I reading? This is not said or answered lightly and therefore, I am, in respect of our old platonic friendship, sending you my hobby, my version of the De Rerum Natura. Being you, I don't have to explain the Latin (Of the Nature of Things), or the author (obviously Lucretius, "thought–son" of Epicurus, the famous pleasure seeker). **This** is what I've been reading and thinking about, while drinking.

De Rerum Natura

This is a compilation of statements that have contributed to my view of "the nature of things". Books obviously have done so, especially those quoted from, but others as well. The quotations come from memory both directly (checked where possible) and indirectly from memories of marked passages in books and other such sources, which I then refer to.

Why these statements? Clearly one does not start with a "worldview" that commends certain statements and rejects others. And of course I have read and heard many things that apparently did not seem both valid and memorable. Some statements no doubt have their affect because they seem inherently plausible (how is that criterion formed?), but many could not pass even that shaky test. A few are scientific statements, reflecting my belief (what caused this belief?) in the overriding importance of science, but most are obviously not propositions that can be tested by the scientific method. Many appealed to me because they strike me as funny or stated with style, as well as being true. But these criteria are already part of a worldview in a sense. The motivation for including some quotations is that they seem to correct a view I was angry at having been misinformed about, probably in school. (For example, Plato's Republic seems more a blueprint for a totalitarian state than the noble ideal I was taught that it is). Clearly we are in Deep Water with the question "why these statements and not others?"

My view of the way things are obviously is not presented as Revealed Truth. The scientific statements can be or have been confirmed by science, but others fall under the cloudy rubric of Taste (except perhaps they can be connected to scientific propositions). And a great many people do not accept science, even when they think they do. (People with degrees in science often hold flagrantly unscientific beliefs).

I do feel strongly that views diverging significantly from my most basic views may well constitute a threat to the health, wealth, and happiness of mankind, but I do not believe that the grounds for this feeling are unassailable. And part of my worldview is gratitude at living in a society where such differences can be examined.

It will be enjoyable to learn what inclusions seem odd or "wrong" to others, particularly those close to me, and what omissions they would require to bring this compilation closer to their concept of the nature of things.

The ordering of quotations is somewhat haphazard; the inclusion of quotations expressing similar ideas is intentional as is that of ones that qualify or occasionally contradict others. Lucretius' coverage of the subject was not complete (his poem was unfinished); obviously, this never will be either. It will be added to as memory pulls up more quotations.

Love, Fabio

Chapter Five

Dear Fabio:

Do you still subscribe to the New Yorker magazine? If you do, you will have learned that you are far from alone in doting on De Rerum Natura. I received your welcome tome of this name, and amazing things have happened. If you have not gotten this month's magazine do just buy it. Devour The Answer Man by Stephen Greenblatt. Is this a coincidence? (I am one of those who don't believe there are such things as coincidences.) It is a gift. To us!

Of course I ran to Google, without reading yours, to the original (Lucretius) DRN and ended up shrieking into the night. Without Greenblatt I would have been eaten alive by those poetic words. It is a POEM, Fabio. Yours is not a poem, unless you define poem as a much broader speech form than I do.

Greenblatt loves the poem. He calls it " the classical account of the material universe, written about a thousand years before Christ", after it was discovered by a Florentine named Poggio Bracciolini in 1417 in a monastery library. In the fullness of time the Lucretius was discovered by Machiavelli, by Jefferson, who owned at least five Latin editions of De Rerum Natura along with translations of the poem into English, Italian, and French. The work influenced Darwin, of course Jefferson, and even Einstein. (**And**, Mr. Greenblatt has written a book about De Rerum by Lucretius called "The Swerve", about how the world became modern. I found it on my Kindle.)

Your Rerum falls short of that, but I can see why you called it that. Someday do a "content analysis" of your Rerum and organize by topic, so it is clearer what vast parts of life you have covered. I miss statements such as " what is man's and nature's true raison d'etre: 'the passionate urge to reproduce its kind'." I know you agree with this but you take it and other grandiosities for granted. You are on a different plane of life, ours, and I accept that, but your Rerum are things of the Twentieth and Twenty-First century, not of the universe at large.

I have looked for similarities in the two Rerums, and there is one very nice one. But 1st is Greenblatt's summary of the six books of the poem (7400 lines; thank you, Stephen Greenblatt). "It yokes together moments of intense lyrical beauty, philosophical meditations on religion, pleasure, and death; and scientific theories of the physical world, the evolution of human societies, the perils and joys of sex and the nature of disease." Oh boy, Lucretius' poem begins with a florid paean to Venus! But, "the philosophy of pleasure, at once passionate, scientific, and visionary, radiates from almost every line of Lucretius' poetry." **And** "the core of Lucretius' poem is a profound, therapeutic meditation on the fear of death." Lucretius despised and held the fear of death in contempt. Remember, Fabio, we have discussed this very thing more than once. Death as a part of life, a fixture in the very Thing we are.

Well, here is a poem by Emily Dickinson on your page seven: which embodies Lucretius' beliefs;

> *The heart asks pleasure first,*
> *And then, excuse from pain;*
> *And then, those little anodynes*
> *That deaden suffering;*
> *And then, to go to sleep;*
> *And then, if it should be*
> *The will of its Inquisitor,*
> *The liberty to die.*

SEE? Pleasure and fearless death.

I see you as a Lucretius. I had even thought of calling a book "Me and The Lucretius" or even "Luc and me", which you would hate. But never mind. Continue with your thing, Luc.

Love, Claudia

P.S. Do you think Emily Dickenson was an Epicurean? (Of course you know Epicurus was Lucretius' guru, the original pleasure-lover). Jefferson said **he** was epicurean. **You** are. I am. And so is Stephen Greenblatt!

P.P.S. Your Rerum suffers from a weird literary form called ibidism.

Chapter Six

Dear Fabio again,

Your Rerum has made an amazing thing come to pass: I have read (in part) The Holmes Pollock Letters. Poor dead Jim would be pleased. I'll quote a letter which you would not have read, in love as you and Jim were with the torts and trusts. This letter shows a lovely masculine feeling and a long true friendship I found wonderful.

> *Washington, March 21, 1931*
>
> *My dear Pollock:*
>
> *In the dense pressure of the last two weeks I fear that I have said nothing of what you wrote for the Columbia Law Review, received only in these last days. Friendship for a moment became articulate and uttered tender and moving things. Of course we have known the friendship long. It is part of my life. But to hear the note of affection along with praises that are so precious when they come from you, is a surprise in spite of all that I know without being told. It would put heart into a brass andiron and I shall die the happier for it.*
>
> *My love to Lady Pollock.*
>
> *Yours ever,*
> *O. W. Holmes*

But wait. We could go on about Holmes-Pollock. But, I **must** return to my first question of the "Fabio and Claudia Reformation". Have you forgotten the first question I posed to you? No, of course not. You thought you had managed to make me forget, didn't you?

Well I did not, and honor makes me answer **my** part of the question.

Why didn't I fall in love with **you**? The answer is, of course, I did.

It was like a movie I bet you didn't see, called "My Best Friend's Wedding". About us, really. About Claudia and Fabio, going way back, taking for granted they would always be there as each other's favorite. Then the Fabio character tells the Claudia character he is going to marry another, and she can't cope with this. Apparently he has just not seen the relationship the way she did, and she is forced to admit it. He was "in love" with the other girl; he was only "in like" with her.

It was not **exactly** the same. I did not actually protest; you did not confide in me. It was a fait-accompli before I could protest. But I knew it was wrong. I still do. I await your answer, thinking of our customary e-mail ending "love, Claudia" and "love, Fabio". Now, perhaps your "love Fabio" is what linguists call phatic communication, as in "how are you" on meeting after a lapse. You don't really expect to hear how they are. I don't expect love, really. There are many phatics, and maybe you don't mean "love" at all. But **I** do, so answer!

Love, Claudia

Chapter Seven

Dear Claudia,

You are right, I had hoped you had forgotten that first question, but, no, I really knew you wouldn't. My answer is "Button up your overcoat," as the answer will freeze you, I'm afraid. I've always been your best friend, always enjoyed parlaying and arguing with you more than with anyone else. But, I did not see LOVE. Why? Because, frankly, I always felt you were in danger of running off or dancing off with the gypsies. Don't you remember that bozo that you used to go out with (whom your mother didn't like because he was a poor student, and how on earth did she check up on him?) He was a dilatory guy, in general. You 2 used to go to that bar called "The Yacht Club" with the slot machine, with friends of his friends. Drink Cokes, and dance to the Nickelodeon. (How did <u>I</u> check up on **you**? Ha!) I felt I knew only part of you, Claudia, the other part was——just beyond me! You are so smart, so semi–scholarly, and always at the top of your class, while Joe What's his name was always held over.

We had such fun dating. You always showed up at school proms and private parties with Jim or me or some other one of our gang, and not Joe Blow. We were our version of snobbish. I never mentioned those periodic Yacht Club episodes though other people gossiped about them and wondered what the hell goes on. It was, of course, none of my business. (Now tell, what **did** go on?) As you said, we were too cool to discuss our private lives. Men, or boys as we were, didn't talk about "like" and "love".

Now, phatic-schmatic, don't force me to give up "love Fabio"! I like it. Don't force me to give it up just to define our relationship, which can't be defined anyway. Look: "yours truly, Fabio." Boring!

Love, Fabio

Chapter Eight

Dear Fabio,

Ye gods, people talked did they! Well, Fabio, in those days dancing itself was phatic. That's what we did instead of discuss the books we were reading, though I danced a lot with you and Jim and **we** unbelievably **did** discuss books while dancing. You, and Jim, I meant to say you, darling, and Jim didn't dance. Really you just **strode** grandly thru the room. Great tall boys not realizing what dancing was, not exactly off-beat, just non-beat or a-beat. Joe Blow, as you call him was an incredible dancer. We did jitterbug like pros, just short of his throwing me up in the air. There wasn't room in that ironically named Yacht Club up the river (Yacht Club, yes, for canoes.) With a heck of a good collection of jitterbug "music".

Fabio, I loved dancing the jitterbug. It was pure joy, especially with Joe Blow. I don't remember any book he read, in fact I don't remember our even talking, but I do remember the other kids applauded us when we danced.

I am on a cane now, for balance only, but I would drop it if a real dancer, like the bozo, came along. It wasn't gypsies I would run away with and Joe never asked me. I never met a "real dancer", except once I hired a Latin dancer to teach me to tango. I really couldn't afford him twice. Yes, I suppose there were 2 sides to Claudia, but Fabio, the dancing Claudia doesn't exist anymore and what I believe to be the real Claudia loves you still. Can't we—? Won't you—?

Love, Claudia

Chapter Nine

Dear Claudia,

No, no, no, stop that slop. Be done with it. I love my Jane, she saved me, she does for me, and I would never hurt her and I don't **want** to.

Love, Fabio

Chapter Ten

Dear Fabio,

Slop? That's me "slop chat, and chop and slat". As they say now, "Whatever."

I know what you want of me. I want this of you too; but more. What you want is an extended **Dual** Rerum. That is pretty much what we have always had before.

I will engage upon it beginning with "I read a good book recently and saw the movie, "The Help". All people, I mean all friends, read it and discussed it. I wondered mainly if things between black and white people still existed like this, and I want to tell you what a friend told me about it. She had been in Georgia and had some horror stories. Here is one about a middle aged Uncle Tom, who was taking care of an old white man, the father of a family. He was at death's door, and barely able to eat, barely able to speak; he lay dying.

The timing was bad for the old man's family. They had planned to travel to the Caribbean, where they had spent some time as semi-members of a fancy club. Now, they were due to attend a cocktail party with all the club members, to test them for **complete membership**, Hooray!

Dad's illness couldn't have come at a worse time. They said to Tom "Could you keep Dad alive until we get back? Its just part of a weekend."

"Yawl gots to know he tired, he don't want no more of this foolishment" said Tom. "Yawl best pray that he go on to the better place now."

The family seemed a bit chastised, but went ahead to the Carribean. Tom, speaking to another servant, said, "Man, them rich folks is sooooome fucked up."

He kept Dad alive, barely, and the family then planned a grand funeral, insisting Tom appear at the funeral. They gave him $400 to buy a proper suit.

Tom dressed for the funeral. Enter a rather spoiled, flirtatious young girl, raving to Tom about his appearance. "A beautiful suit, and it is the real you, Tom." She ran her hands down his arms, and said, "Tom, you've got price tags tucked into your sleeves, for heaven's sake. You should have gotten rid of them. You don't want people to think you had to buy a new suit just for the funeral." She promptly pulled out the offending tags and tore them up.

"There you're perfect," she said, as Tom realized he wouldn't be able to return the $400 suit tomorrow, after all. **And** he was out of a job.

I guess he was a "driving Miss Daisy man" but we've gotten too used to thinking things are different, all the unpleasant stuff is past. We have elected a half black president. Did you also feel ecstatic when Obama was elected? Were you really high on feeling we have proved to the world that we are truly democratic?

The bloody melting pot is multi-racial and proud of it. We have arrived.

I wish Obama well and hate his having it uphill all the way, attacked by the economy, jobs, wars, and Republicans.

I heard a lecture about Obama the other day, his elegance, his stability, his presence. His mistakes in the 1st year in office. His concentration on a left–type project in the face of the central-to-right population. The lack of CEOs in his cabinet, which other CEO's, it was said, helped FDR. Obama faced an equally difficult country.

Needless to say the audience exploded in approval of **Obama's bad luck**. Also at a joke disparaging Harvard. The audience was Yale, and that's not all.

But the speaker said JFK had made some mistakes in his 1st year, too. And Obama is apt to reach his central position and begin to win, as in JFK and the Cuban missile crisis. Silence, from the audience.

Well I am worried, aren't you? Worried about Obama, terrorists, who are determined to kill, not caring about other's lives or their own, the US's determination to go on being second-class or worse as long as its people can go on living the sweet life. Do you feel nervous? Do you feel worried too?

Love, Claudia

Chapter Eleven

Dear Claudia,

It has been 2 months, goodbye silly season. And you did write such a challenging letter. But today I will just answer your worry question and then we will return to being "above it all". I mean, we can't afford to waste this time trying to solve impossible problems. Pretty soon you will be thinking about The Rapture and the Mayan calendar. The End of the World. I did Google it (world's end) the other day, and I was promised a publication. I was disappointed in what came up, but Google is only human, after all, damn it.

You may wonder how I happened to go this way in my thinking at all, as it is far from "my way" or "Lucretius' way". But I am only human, too, and I did have an existential problem called a heart by-pass, followed by a staph infection, and began to think about "the end."

I haven't wanted to mention it again, because it is all over now. I lived. I began to flourish. But, it suggested the early retirement, which you might have wondered about. You can understand, however, that your talk of LOVE now seemed ridiculous.

It was not all that bad, worse for Jane of course, and helped us to decide to move to California.

Now that I have gone into it, I'd just as soon not discuss it, or "the end". You and I have no fear of it, Luc and I agree wholeheartedly. But, dear Claudia, we are over seventy years old, and this occurs to me often. "Four score and ten..." It is too late except for friendship.

Love, Fabio

Chapter Twelve

Dear Fabio:

Don't you realize that seventy is the new forty now and it appears
—I think—you have indeed risen above existential problems now.
I have great hopes for you. I had not realized quite how down you
have been, and now I know I have placed undue added stress on you.
My time was not your time, and I will let you catch up. As you will,
Fabio.

Back to safety: what are you reading (poor darling)?

Love, Claudia

Chapter Thirteen

Dear Claudia,

My almost thoughtful old friend. Thank you. Thank you. Thank you.

I am reading, re-reading for the umpteenth time, Tristram Shandy. Have you re-read, or just read, or horrors, never read Tristram Shandy?

I will pause, now, for a few days. We are going to visit offspring. I'll get back to you in a week or so. Meanwhile, check out T. S.

Love, Fabio

Chapter Fourteen

Dear Fabio,

We have never discussed Tristram Bloody Shandy because—oh horrors—I have tried and failed. I looked it up on my Kindle, making it so easy, no excuse. But dammit, I just can't do it. I have gone 10 pages before, (but the Kindle doesn't count pages, dammit) a few times. Tell me why I must read it. Make me proceed.

Welcome back and love, Claudia

P.S. Don't go. I have to tell you an old Shandy tale. I was reading along hopefully, yawningly, when all of a sudden I saw the word Singularity. Not "The Singularity", which I believe you know from Kurzweil. Just singularity.

I was caught up short. At first I thought—well, I thought he was talking MODERN. I stopped yawning and read. "Singularity is the three great essentials of matter, form, and place." Pretty good for the 17th century, or is it? I don't get it.

I looked for my old file on Kurzweil and The Singularity and found the good New York Times piece, called **Merely Human, That's So Yesterday** (did you see it?) which said, (well, you probably remember) "The Singularity is a time possibly just a couple decades from now (June 12, 2010 was "now"), when a superior intelligence will dominate and life will take on an altered form that we can't predict or comprehend in our current limited state, when human beings and machines will so elegantly and effortlessly merge, that poor health, the ravages of old age and even death itself will all be things of the past."

Then I began to look up the word in Google, Wikipedia, and my iPhone and found mention of—are you prepared? The Black Hole. One said The Singularity is the final state of matter falling into a black hole. Others had matter **in** the black hole. I swear! The point is that **<u>The Singularity is Near</u>** has been published but not yet read by me.

I am willing to leave The Singularity and Kurzweil to the angels, skip over the T. Shandy singularity, and try to carry on, thinking of all the famous people including one of my favorites, Jefferson, who loved T. S. and try, try, again.

Love, Claudia

Chapter Fifteen

Dear Claudia,

Well, back at you. I don't know from singularity though I have read in a book called **The Age of Spiritual Machines** by Kurzweil where he didn't mention the S word, nor did the book's index.

Funny; I thought of another word now bandied about: RENDITION. I thought singularity is treated like "rendition" and went off irrelevantly (like you) into a bit of etymology (I think). This word, rendition used to mean a performance, or an interpretation but now to many of us it means an abduction and removal to a foreign country which permits torture. I got all excited about my journey into etymology, until I thought of a few words like balls, dykes etc. which do the same thing.

I race back to T.S.: yes, you have to read it. I order you to proceed and predict you will do a U-turn and agree with me that it is hilariously funny, desperately serious, and agrees with you on war.

Love, Fabio

Chapter Sixteen

Dear Fabio:

Happy Valentines Day, u r my valentine.

I just **can't** let it go to the angels. I have found it in the physicists. I sometimes think I should just drop everything for as many years as it takes and try to learn physics. I am always sneaking around at its borderland with philosophy, with math, yes, with music, pretending I am "real", but I am far from it.

I've been reading a book on the history of science, which I am not prepared to understand any more than I did Dawkins, Brian Greene, et. al., which I have wrestled with for years. But this book has The Singularity, loud and clear.

The Beginning of Infinity by David Deutsch it is. Doesn't mention Kurtzweil, but begins instead with a man named Vernor Vinge, who wrote a book in 1993 called The Coming Technological Singularity, defining it as an event beyond which superhuman minds will be constructed. There will be AI (artificial intelligence), and Vinge states that; "The human era will be over".

Well, David Deutsch doesn't buy this. You will understand him better than I do, she said modestly, but he deals with The Singularity interestingly. It may have been—note this, Fabio—The Big Bang may have been a case of it, and black holes come into it, as I found out from multiple definitions early on.

You would really have to read this book to understand why (D.D. believes) The Singularity isn't going to happen. But, Fabio, don't miss this book. I am half through it. Catch up to me.

Love, Claudia

Chapter Seventeen

Dear Claudia:

You have scared me shitless. I have to admit I am not up to it, and I hate The Singularity! I've tried, I've tried. I retrieved that NY Times article. Do you know that there is a Singularity University, which hundreds of supposedly smart people are fighting to get in against the barrier of a "limited-persons" and a cost of $25,000 per place. One of the co-founders of Google helped set up the University in 2008. The other co-founder (who, it says here became part man and part machine at a NASA campus. What? Let me see.) And some of the believers think that humans will eventually break into two groups, the Haves with superior intelligence, who can live for hundreds of years, versus the Have-nots, who are hampered by antiquated corporeal forms and beliefs.

Now Claudia, we might be two of those people, fighting to get in. Determined to be Haves. Let me save you from this unmitigated horror, and I **know** you need saving.

Couldn't we just acknowledge that there are things we cannot know? Our damned default includes things we can't, haven't, will never never know. We become ridiculous trying to know. Who knows what would happen if we tried and failed? Worse, perhaps, if we tried and succeeded. Can't we be Adam and Eve but with inhuman foresight? Just say "NO" to all that (except Adam and Eve).

I don't apologize; cite getting too old to join your hi-jinks. I don't have time, Claudia.

Maybe you are beginning again to be that second Claudia I long ago forebode to try and know. Now you have a chance to stop jitter-bugging. Reject the Apple!

Love, Fabio

Chapter Eighteen

Dear Fabio:

What do you mean you don't have time? You've plenty of time for Adam and Eve.

Well, yes you do, if you just finally follow through with Adam and Eve. At last, you are on the way. Being Adam and my being Eve. Have we not been working up to this?

All right, we'll let Vinge/Kurtzie/et al. be the Apple; we agree at last.

Love, Claudia

Chapter Nineteen

Dear Claudia:

No, no, stop twisting everything. This only means you will go back with me to the Dual Rerum. Your words, Love them. I'll be Lucretius and you be Lucretia. Forget Adam and Eve, those old hats at the beginning of time. We'll start with Pogo and The Swerve, loving life, concentrating on beauty, wine and absolute music.

I know, That's so Human. But watch out, The Singularity is near! I cannot believe how near. I won't! The word "on the street" is that APPLE has hired Kurtzwell to be its head of research. Or will hire. Oh no! Forget this. It can not be true!

Join me or leave me. I mean it.

Love, Fabio

PART II:
After two-month silence from both

Chapter Twenty

Dear Claudia:

Think not of the long silence but of the friendship returned. You will be surprised at my discussion of Bruckner, whom I have never before listened to. After a good conversation with a good musical friend (an absolute good friend, may I say) who told me that Bruckner was by way of a precursor to Mahler. I bought Bruckner's Ninth.

You remember, I suppose, the saga of the Ninth, which has kept me away. It is three reputedly magnificent movements, but before the 4th and last, he died. Early, I think, and well. He just slipped away in his sleep, good fortune I envy.

A lot has been going on for 25 years in Bruckneriana. Many have written the 4th movement, all unsuccessful. My friend told me that the symphony I bought had a fourth movement, but he was sorry to report that it wasn't any good, or even Brucknerish. So Jane and I decided just to not play the Fourth.

The 3 Bruckner movements were in every way wonderful, yes. I thought the Mahlerish and a bit Schubertish and Wagner-ish parts and other parts were monumental. I can't remember you ever discussing Anton Bruckner, but now I am giving you a gift: pour a glass of good red wine and listen to Bruckner's 9th, movements, 1, 2 and 3.

I am glad to be back in touch and hope you will be too. Nothing important has happened to me (or us) or to our offspring, so I can report that all is well here on the shelf.

Love, Fabio

Chapter Twenty-One

Dear Fabio: (immediately)

I am glad too. Were we fighting? I've almost forgotten why. I do have to say that I feel you have somewhat changed: you would never have left that Bruckner 9th 4th movement unheard. No criticism; just thank you for trying to save me.

Thanks for the true gift. I borrowed the symphony from the library and listened to all of it. Of course. You were right: the 4th almost spoils it. What did I get for being—what—more nervy then you? A falling off of respect for nervy.

I am still here and I promise I will not engage you in unnamed S, and I assure you that I'm not standing in line to get into S University. I don't promise never to read about it or even to mention it, but I do promise that I am not hooked. And of course, as between you and K and even D, I choose you.

Love, Claudia

Chapter Twenty-Two

Dear Fabio **again**: This is not a first.

I have read a book with a tantalizing title: Why Mahler? Skipping quickly over the expected Why Not Mahler? Why Why Mahler? And similar japes, I discovered the author's Why. Because he read Alma Mahler's memoir of her marriage to Mahler, which led said author to find out about a man who inspired such **passionate ambivalence**. There. You are sold too on passionate ambivalence.

Mahler was unique in that he told conductors to play his pieces anyway they liked, as they found the particular musicality of halls, their acoustics, the size of audiences, and so on. No composer had granted this license before. It makes each concert a world premiere, different from the others by up to 10 minutes.

I want to listen to the "**universality**" (you get rock music, movie music), the "**conflict and contradiction in one piece**", and the "**irony**" in his music. I would like to be able to feel these things specifically and, in particular, its claimed **application to the 21st century**. The author says Mahler's music unlocks expression, colors, dreams, leads to a self-awareness that, in turn, leads to self-content. This is Mahler's contribution to the modern world. Aren't you glad we love Mahler and accept his contribution with thanks? This book sounds like a beguiled and bedazzled concert description. I'll buy it all, without being there!

Love, Claudia

Chapter Twenty-Three

May 10th

Dear Claudia:

I am trying to get Why Mahler? I hate my library today; they don't have it, but promised. In the meantime I have returned again to Mozart, mainly because of the discussion of his influence on small babies and children. Which leads inevitably to "what <u>is</u> music"? It is one of the greatest mysteries of life, everyone's life, but forgive me, especially my life. Let me ponder it again until the book comes.

Love, Fabio

Chapter Twenty-Four

Dear Fabio:

Oh, first I must tell you how happy I am to revisit the effect of music upon one of my children. I brought him home from the hospital and set him up in his crib in the room next to us parents, put him on his stomach to sleep (as we did then) and on his back to learn about life. One day I put on not Mozart but Brahms, sentimentally, the Brahms' Lullaby.

I worked up to symphonies. All of Brahms was successful. I can still see in my mind's eye his tiny, pinkish face now, as I put the needle to the record and it began to play. There was his first real smile (he was less than a month old.) It was beautiful, and music always "worked".

Of course, I tried other composers, including Mozart but not focusing on him, dammit, or I could have contributed to the current conversation. But Fabio, I feel you pondering. I ponder, too, and often. What the hell **is** music?

I have checked out "music" in a book I leave by my bed, ready for all philosophy conundrums. Do you know Brian McGee, Confessions of A Philosopher? He is a popularizer, but sophisticated, and almost possible to understand, i.e. difficult enough to seem legit.

McGee says that the greatest achievement in the history of philosophy was Kant's. I have to go into this to get to music (though you may know all about it): the difference between the phenomenal and the noumenal.

There is a word missing here; those two difficult words are adjectives, so we need a noun or two. Phenomenal things; noumenal things? What Google says: is the noumenal things "in the philosophy of Kant, an object **as it is in itself** independent of the mind, as opposed to a phenomenon." Also called a thing in itself, or in German "ding an sic."

The phenomenal is what we believe is the real thing, everyday things, science and philosophy (if they can be said to be "everyday"). The noumenal is out there beyond, somewhat like Plato's "forms", not phenomenal, but the really more world we never actually see.

Did we learn all this stuff in Philosophy 101? Learn? Ha. Don't think I know what I'm talking about, but I love talking of it.

But we have to look at Kant or give up. And now, see Schopenhauer! He was the greatest explicator and corrector of Kant, according to McGee. He believed that music was actually noumenological, and, in this, different from all the other arts. Therefore, not intelligible or explainable. But it **is**, **I** am saying, feelable. Can the noumenological realm be feelable? If so, I will spend the rest of my life finding something else besides music which is feelable and also noumenological. Whew!

Ha! Have I just added to human knowledge or fallen flat upon my face? Chose one.

Down here on my face I am forced to remark surlily, "if science is really not the ding an sic, not independent of our minds, (how ridiculous), I am going to cease looking hopefully for the Higgs boson!"

Love, Claudia

P.S. The Higgs has often been called the God particle. So, ipso facto, God is also a product of our minds. Say "**only** a product of our minds." Who wants to be the one to add that to human knowledge?

Chapter Twenty-Five

Dear Claudia:

You must be tired of my telling you wistfully that I don't have time. I would like to join you and Kant and Schopenhauer and spend our literary lives searching for a little bit of the noumenal realm. Yes. But I really **don't** have time to specialize. You remember that I'm of the "can't know" school of auto–didacticism. Let me go on with my Lucretius and drop you a random up-date on whatever I fall upon in my travels. Don't be discouraged. (I'll hear about this. "I bet you have lots of time for other things; so give me some.")

So, I have a startling proposal, which you should hang on to loyally, and stop pushing me hither and yon, fascinating as that is. You **can believe** that a year from today, more or less, but **really**, we two will actually meet. Maybe in your place. Maybe in the old Palisades Park, why not? And then, we will truly recapture the friendship you remember.

Love, Fabio

Chapter Twenty-Six

Dear Fabio: (By return email)

You have my attention. Of course that's what I want — "my desire", (But why so long? All right, I'll wait, but....)

Oh Fabio, I **knew** you would come around, and you **did**, my hero! No, no, take it back, you love your wife. Don't worry, I am "hip".

Oh, but can I wait? Now that I **know**, oh Fabio, a whole year? I can't imagine what we will discuss for a year. Plans For The Palisades?

Love, Claudia

Chapter Twenty-Seven

Dear Claudia: (also BRE)

If you **are** hip, and I trust you, you will restrain yourself and obey my only request: this year will be **mine, mine**. And you will admit you know what "mine" is, a year without histrionics. **Just like the old Palisades**, we will share books and ideas with Love Lost. It is important to me. **Can** you do it?

Love, Fabio

Chapter Twenty-Eight

Dear Fabio: **Proof** that I can

Speaking of "end–times" as we once were doing, I am happy, happy to record a la Rerum, a quote from Elaine Pagel's new book, Revelations:

> *"The book of Revelation is the strangest book in the Bible and the most controversial.*
> *Instead of stories and moral teaching, it offers only visions—dreams and nightmares. And although few people say they understand it's powerful images and processes, the book has been wildly popular among readers for two thousand years. Even today, countless people throughout the world turn to it to find meaning, and many Christian groups claim to see its prophecies and divine judgment being fulfilled before their eyes. Millions fear being 'left behind' when the end comes ------- and believe that they are seeing its prophesied battles playing out in catastrophic events of recent history. It's visions of heaven and hell weave through literature from Milton's, Paradise Lost to the poems of William Butler Yeats and the stories of James Baldwin, and have inspired music ranging from 'Battle Hymn of the Republic' and African-American spirituals to the Quartet for the End of Time, which French composer Olivier Messiaen wrote and first performed in an Nazi prison camp. Filmmakers and artists today graphically picture its visions, as Michelangelo, Goya, Bosch, Blake, and Picasso did before them. Christians in America have identified with its visions of cosmic*

wars since the 1600s, when many immigrating to the new world believed they had arrived in the 'new Jerusalem' promised in Revelation. Many have seen America as 'redeemer nation' that is to bring in the millennium, while others see its military and economic system as evil Babylon. Political rhetoric still appeals to our nation's sense of divine destiny—or damns America for its sins."
You gotta love it, like music.

Love, Claudia (See?)

Chapter Twenty-Nine

Dear Fabio:

"End–times", we were not discussing, just mentioning. You are giving me the creeps with your "no time left" stuff. Yet you promise the future, which I cleave to loyally, as you requested in your letter on June 20th.

Yes, the Pagels is marvelous, and is clearing up a lot of things for me. I now have it, en–Kindle thank you, Fabio. I went immediately to chapter three. Have you read it all? Probably. If not, press on to the part about Christianity itself. Pagels is so clever, so unsanctimonious, so historical, Brava!

Anyway, she discusses the Christianity of Paul of Tarsus, moving on the Gentiles, departing radically from John of Patmos (of this book). John wrote around 90 C. E. worried that the holy people (Israel's "saving remnant") were being infiltrated by outsiders who had no regard for Israel's purity.

John stood on the cusp of an enormous change, which would eventually transfer the entire movement from a Jewish messianic sect into Christianity. With Paul's help, including Greeks, Asians, Africans, Gauls, Germans, Spaniards, and Egyptians.

But, since that hadn't happened yet, at least among John's audience in Asia Minor, he took his stand as a Jewish prophet, charged with keeping God's holy people holy, unpolluted by Roman culture. Jesus twice warns his followers in Asia Minor to beware of "Blasphemers", who say they are Jews and are not and so are not of God's people. They are a "Synagogue of Satan". These people discussed how much or whether to assimilate, and there were two major differences concerning diet (whether to eat meat that had been sacrificed, unclean meat) or permit fornication (unclean sex or even marriage). The question of insisting on circumcision, which Paul did not!

Some scholars say that John was a Christian by the time he wrote his book, that Judaism and Christianity were separate, and that Judaism as a powerful tradition effectively came to an end about 70 C. E. John's lifetime spanned the transition but never in this book did he say he was a Christian.

Some say the term Christian was coined by German magistrates to identify Gentiles who were treasonous to Rome.

Paul encouraged his Gentiles to believe that if they were baptized Christian they became Israeli and were the heirs of Jesus's chosen people.

John (and obviously Pagels) thought that this was the **greatest identity theft of all time**.

Isn't this a marvelous upgrade to modern lexicography?

Love, Claudia

Chapter Thirty

Dear Claudia:

What a good exchange, reading the same book simultaneously, noting the differences and similarities of our interests. Let's do that again, like "set your watches; begin!" Only better. The Pagels was a good book with which to try this out. We were as close or closer than we will be at the Palisades. I have not forgotten, in either sense. You want me to feel; I feel... close.

I would like to propose a new end–of–career book by Warren Phillips, called, Newspaperman, rather than "la de-da" Journalist. An important editor, producer, boss of bosses, and in old friend of mine, with Good Character. I am giving you an appropriate part of his book, called Reporters, Readers, and the Pursuit of Trust:

> *"Polls abound showing widespread mistrust of the press. Overcoming that and earning reader trust is a never–ending battle. We took pride in a Harris Poll in August 1969 that found the Wall Street Journal was the most trusted newspaper in America. Even so, as well as people we had written about, who complained we had been inaccurate or unfair or biased in our reporting. Sometimes they were right. Other times their complaints reflected their own prejudices and perspectives, and truth lay in the eye of the beholder.*
>
> *We began the fight for reader trust by trying to hire, train, and retain reporters of skill and integrity, then having not one but several layers of editors scrutinize their work and that of fellow reporters hired regionally by*

local bureau chiefs, but most job candidates wound up being interviewed by me while I was managing editor."

"In addition to examining their resumes and clippings, I asked new college graduates about their grades, thinking it might be one indicator of intelligence—realizing it was only one among many, and imperfect at that. I also asked.......... what pre-interview research they had done about the Journal, might shed light on their potential as good reporters."

Impressive, I think, don't you?

Sorry that's all for today, Claudiator.

Love, Fabio

Chapter Thirty-One

Dear Fabio:

The Newspaperman is on my Kindle, and I have read it. We are in sync. There are many sides to your old friend; here is one quote about his favorite sport.

> *"It was a rough voyage; we came down Narragansett Bay in pea-soup fog, then through turbulent water and steep following seas, in The Race, the famously tricky passage off of Fisher's Island, before entering the more protected waters of Long Island Sound. I preferred sailboats. Like skiing or flying they offered the relative quiet, solitude, peace, and immersion in nature's wonders while alone, or almost so, and the soul-satisfying experience of harnessing natural forces and testing one's skills on one's own."*

Yes, impressive. It might be interesting to hear what his wife says about sailing; with which I agree. "The family that sails together drifts apart."

Fabio, I read a book I would really like you to read, though it is horrible. Here is the background. I've had some horrible dreams for the last year or two, and by chance I heard of a psychologist or psychiatrist (which?) who specializes in dreams. And geriatrics, but who needs that?

She gave me this book to read the first day I spoke to her, and it has dominated my waking life–thank God not my sleeping life–all week. Why, I wonder, considering the events portrayed are so many years ago and so completely experienced—not the events, but the news of them.

It is by Victor Frankel, in two parts: Man's Search for Meaning, part one. Part two: Experiences in a Concentration Camp. Read, please, though I am sorry for the misery.

Love, Claudia

Chapter Thirty-Two

Dear Claudia:

I have the Frankl and I have had it since the War. I read it, over
and over, partly because I had seen an article by much–approved–by–
me Arthur Koestler (remember "Darkness at Noon", which included
this vision: "white breasts in champagne glasses"). He was scolding
people for complaining they had heard too much about the Holocaust:
people should never forget it, should read, see, and hear as much about
the Holocaust as they can, so that it can never happen again!

Well, I did read Frankl; forgive me if I have **stopped** reading it.
I'll just say that one thing Frankl says I remember very well. He spoke
of Thomas Mann's, Magic Mountain to show a situation similar to
life in the camps, an unpromised exit from tuberculosis, **without a
future and a goal**, life going on and on missing the future, falling
into the escapist past.

It occurred to me that other lives are lived where these things hold
true, maybe other sick people who know they are about to die.......
Perhaps soon?

So, we are close again, oddly enough in the Holocaust. Let's
find another subject, maybe your awful dreams. I hate that you are
besieged by tortures, which they really are that, and also they are, I
suspect, post–dramatic–stress–disorders.

We have lived and are living in parlous times, Claude. You are almost as good as a man; so let me sneak this masculinization in by way
of a compliment. That started out to be a joke, opening me to your
wrath, but I can take it, Claude.

Love, Fabio

Chapter Thirty-Three

Darling Fabbie:

I also like the occasional femininities you let slip (regarding **your** masculinization of **me**). As long as we know we are out of line and making jokes which are no longer, or never were, appropriate, and admitting all this, well, you'll let me do it, too.

Fabio, thank you, but let's not get into my dreams. If this psych/ psycho thinks she can help, I will be open to her, but I would be open to you on this subject only if I hadn't started with her.

I was thinking of another one of my faults, chatting. Now don't worry, I got rid of that empty page. I have two books that are appropriate for you to read (or scan) to help me to conquer chatting. First, Quiet, the Power of Introverts in a World that can't Stop Talking, by Susan Cain, and second, Gossip, the Untrivial Pursuit, by Joseph Epstein.

First, Cain quotes an old friend of mine who is dead, but **was** very smart indeed: "Tocqueville saw that the life of constant action and decision which was entailed by the Democratic and business-like character of American life put a premium upon rough and ready habits of mind, quick decision, and the prompt seizure of opportunities–and that all of this activity was not propitious for deliberation, elaboration, or precision in thought." Richard Hofstadter, my pal, "Anti-Intellectualism in America."

I hate being a chatterer, but even more I hate being classed as anti–intellectual.

Second, I read Epstein's book because I loved his other work: "The Kid is Seventy", The Long Unhappy Life of Saul Bellow", et. al. So, I read "Gossip", which I found untypical of him but quite interesting, probably not for you, and watch out, he quotes the Talmud: "Don't speak well of your friend, for although you will start with his good traits the discussion might turn to his bad traits." Well, maybe.

In this, "your time" of our interchange, I need to find more positive works, "happy thoughts". You have made me happy, by telling me we will meet, and that is all–important, but it is not yet upon us, alas.

Goodbye for now with love, Claudia

Chapter Thirty-Four

Dear Claudia:

I do not know your last name; I have never heard of you. I am Jane, Fabio's wife, and alas, he is gone. Has died. Almost a month ago. He had locked his computer, and by the time I got around to getting it on line, time had passed and I finally came upon your name and your address.

I have no idea why you were sent the famous Rerum. This is how I found you: there is, next to his computer a two-step storage place for letters and files, at the bottom of which he had placed the Rerum, marked with a Post-it which said David, George, and Claudia, with only your address and no last names. David is his brother, George probably his best friend, and those addresses were in his memory. So, not understanding "Claudia", I've finally written to you, mainly to send you this poem, which was the only thing on his computer!

He had showed this poem to me already, and said it was on his Rerum but that he had looked at it recently with "new eyes". It occurred to me that if he meant for you to see it, he may not have seen it in the manuscript. He sent you (when?) Or—well, I admit it gave me a brief horror-shock, which was a foolish fear that you and he may be having a long-distance romance. Not the best thing to discover at your beloved husband's death. I just chose to disbelieve this. No one could have been lovelier to me as a husband. Likewise, no woman could have loved him more deeply.

His death was sudden, at home, in the evening. He was at the computer in his study, and must have had a heart attack (again), and fell from his chair. He had reached out to grab a standing lamp next to the desk, and it fell upon his by-this-time lifeless body. I need not tell you how the sight of him, entangled in the lamp and cords upon the floor, made me feel, a sight I keep seeing in my dreams and awake.

> *The heart asks pleasure first,*
>
> *And then, excuse from pain;*
>
> *And then, those little anodynes*
>
> *That deaden suffering;*
>
> *And then, to go to sleep;*
>
> *And then, if it should be*
>
> *The will of its Inquisitor,*
>
> *The liberty to die.*
>
> *Emily Dickinson*

Best Wishes, Jane

Chapter Thirty-Five

Dear Jane:

I can believe how deeply you loved him. I loved him, too, as a childhood friend. We reconnected about a year ago and remembered youthful thoughts and dreams. Thank you for the rather brave approach to a stranger, who can assure you that you were well loved and appreciated. I couldn't forget his first wife, who was so not good enough for him. Forgive me, I hoped you were the same, to my disgrace, but he most certainly showed me that you were not.

I was haunted by the lamp-sight as well, and because I so want to give you something I am sending you a lamp-poem by Shelley, which, for some reason many years ago I committed to memory. There are four stanzas, but you get only the first. Not all of it remains in my mind.

When the Lamp is Shattered
by Percy Bysshe Shelley

When the lamp is shattered
The light in the dust lies dead-
When the cloud is scattered,
The rainbow's glory is shed.
When the lute is broken,
Sweet tones are remembered not;
When the lips have spoken,
Loved accents are soon forgot. (Not true, Claudia)

My best wishes, Claudia

Chapter Thirty-Six

Dear Jane:

Tell me, please, did Fabio know he was soon to go? Did he expect to live—well, another year?

Yours, Claudia

Chapter Thirty-Seven

Claudia:

Another year? More like another month. He was never the same Fabio after a heart operation two years ago, and he steadily worsened, rather than steadily improved. I knew, too. It was agony.

Jane